Journal

ISBN
9781789508598

W0008630

This edition published in 2019 by Arcturus Publishing Limited
26/27 Bickels Yard, 151–153 Bermondsey Street,
London SE1 3HA

Copyright © Arcturus Holdings Limited

All rights reserved. No part of this publication may be reproduced,
stored in a retrieval system, or transmitted, in any form or by any means,
electronic, mechanical, photocopying, recording or otherwise, without
prior written permission in accordance with the provisions of the
Copyright Act 1956 (as amended). Any person or persons who do any
unauthorised act in relation to this publication may be liable to criminal
prosecution and civil claims for damages.

AD007509UK

Printed in the UK

This book is
from the library of

....

....

....

Journal

Journal

Journal

Journal

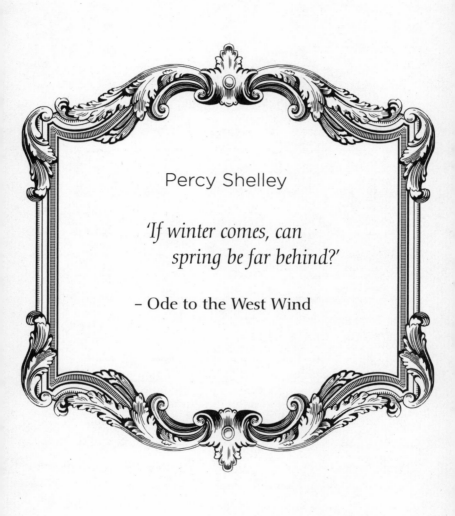

Percy Shelley

*'If winter comes, can
spring be far behind?'*

– Ode to the West Wind

Journal

Journal

Journal

Journal

Journal

Journal

Journal

Journal

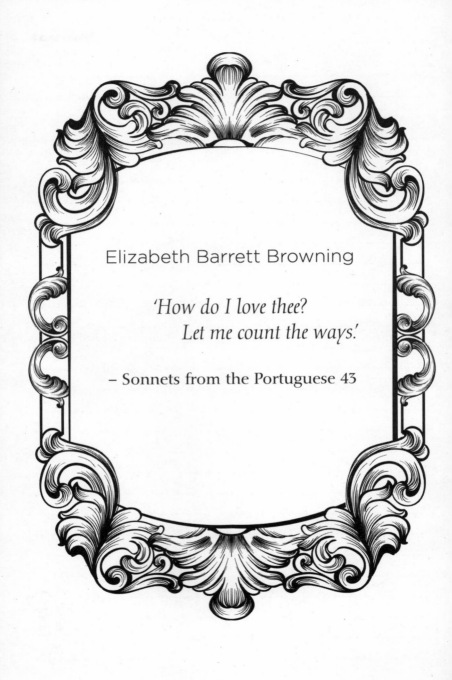

Elizabeth Barrett Browning

'How do I love thee?
  Let me count the ways.'

– Sonnets from the Portuguese 43

Journal

Journal

Journal

Journal

Journal

Journal

Journal

Journal

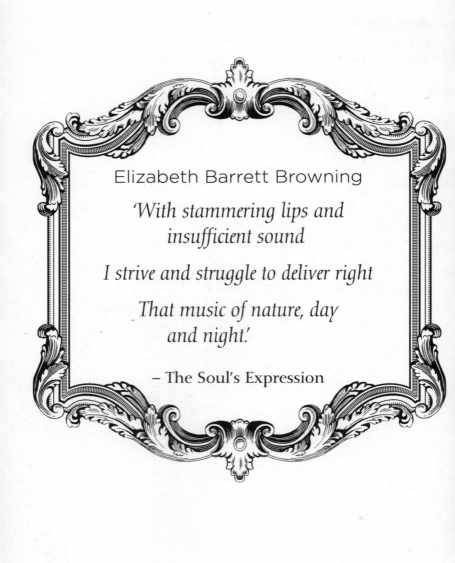

Elizabeth Barrett Browning

'With stammering lips and
insufficient sound

I strive and struggle to deliver right

That music of nature, day
and night.'

– The Soul's Expression

Journal

Journal

Journal

Journal

Journal

Journal

Journal

Journal

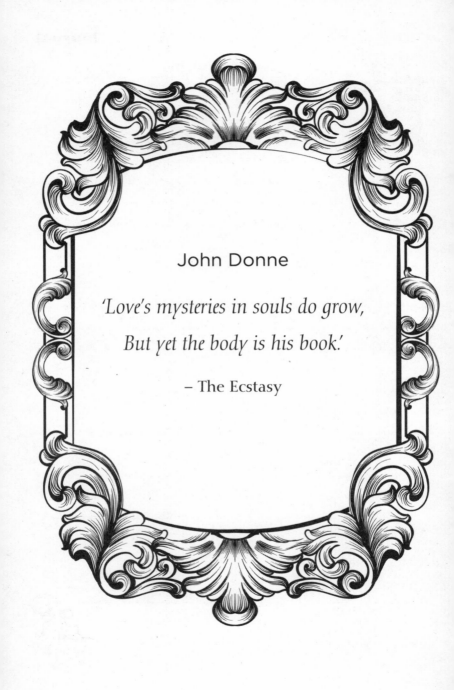

John Donne

'Love's mysteries in souls do grow,
But yet the body is his book.'

– The Ecstasy

Journal

Journal

Journal

E. Shute

Journal

Journal

Journal

Journal

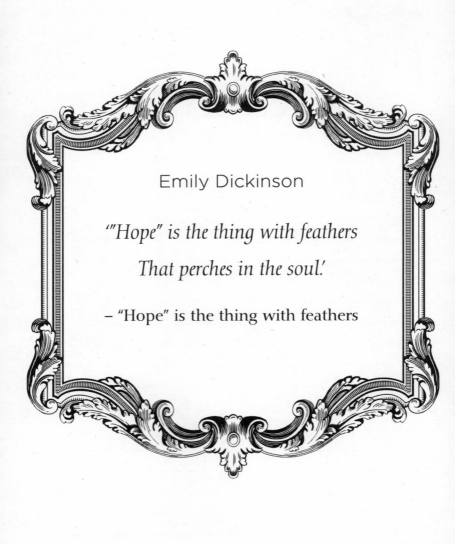

Emily Dickinson

'"Hope" is the thing with feathers
That perches in the soul.'

– "Hope" is the thing with feathers

Journal

Journal

Journal

Journal

Journal

Journal

Journal

Journal

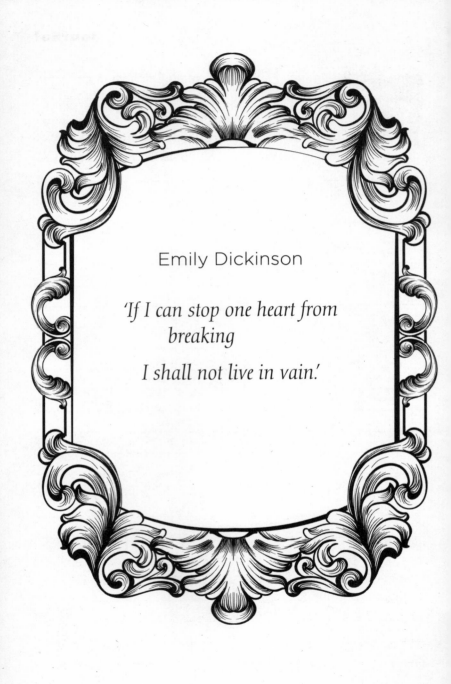

Emily Dickinson

'If I can stop one heart from
breaking

I shall not live in vain.'

Journal

Journal

Journal

Journal

Journal

Journal

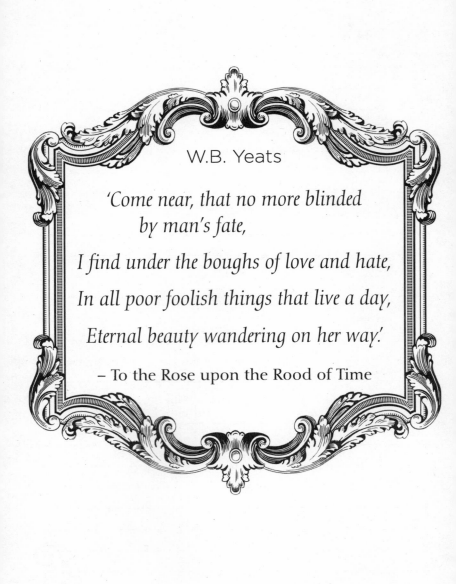

W.B. Yeats

'Come near, that no more blinded
by man's fate,

I find under the boughs of love and hate,

In all poor foolish things that live a day,

Eternal beauty wandering on her way.'

– To the Rose upon the Rood of Time

Journal

Journal

Journal

Journal

Journal

Journal

Journal

Journal

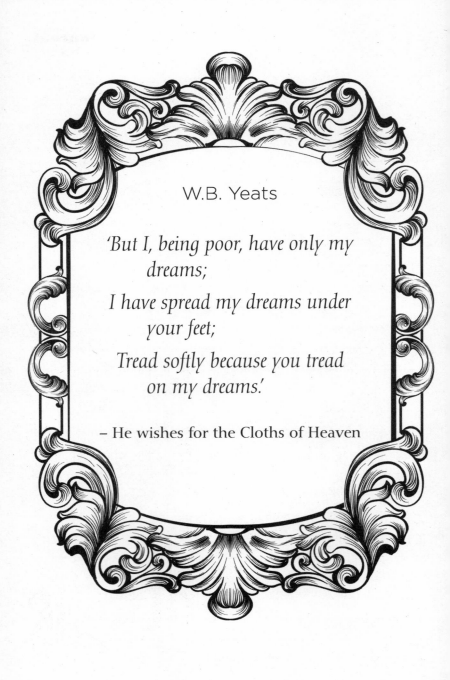

W.B. Yeats

'But I, being poor, have only my
dreams;

I have spread my dreams under
your feet;

Tread softly because you tread
on my dreams.'

– He wishes for the Cloths of Heaven

Journal

Journal

Journal

Journal

Journal

Journal

Journal

Journal

Walt Whitman

'O Captain! My Captain! Our fearful trip is done

The ship has weather'd every rack, the prize we sought is won.'

– O Captain! My Captain!

Journal

Journal

Journal

Journal

Journal

Journal

Journal

Journal

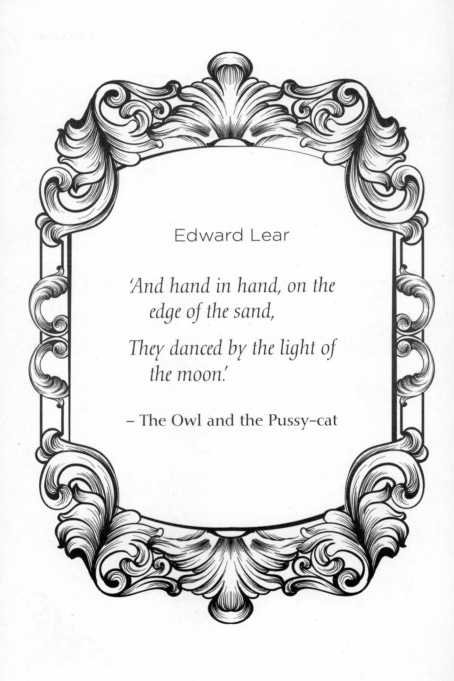

Edward Lear

'And hand in hand, on the edge of the sand,

They danced by the light of the moon.'

– The Owl and the Pussy-cat

Journal

Journal

Journal

Journal

Journal

Journal

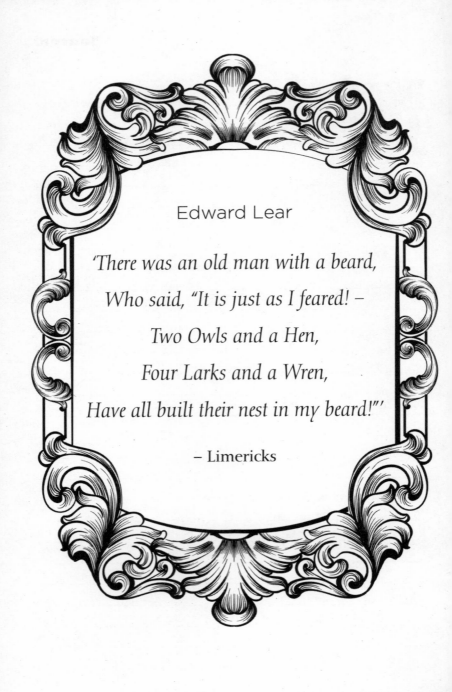

Edward Lear

'There was an old man with a beard,

Who said, "It is just as I feared! –

Two Owls and a Hen,

Four Larks and a Wren,

Have all built their nest in my beard!"'

– Limericks

Journal

Journal

Journal

Journal

Journal

Journal

Oscar Wilde

'Some love too little, some
too long,

Some sell, and others buy;

Some do the deed with many tears,

And some without a sigh.'

– The Ballad of Reading Gaol

Journal

Journal

Journal

Journal

Journal

Journal

Journal

Journal

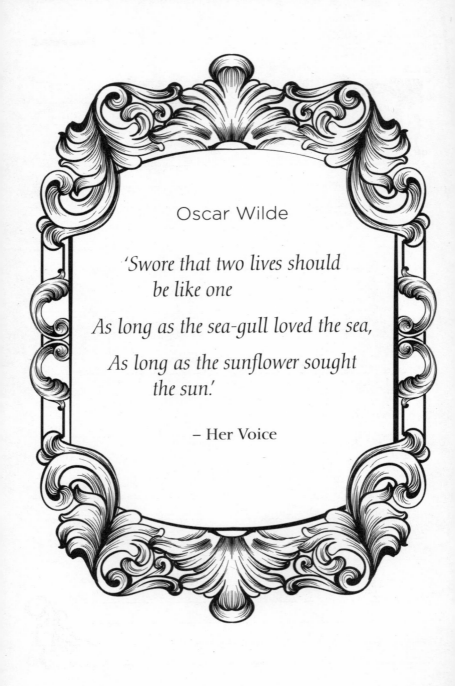

Oscar Wilde

'Swore that two lives should
be like one

As long as the sea-gull loved the sea,

As long as the sunflower sought
the sun.'

– Her Voice

Journal

Journal

Journal

Journal

Journal

Journal

Journal

John Keats

'*Bright star, would I were*
stedfast as thou art–

Not in lone splendour hung
aloft the night.'

– Bright Star

Journal

Journal

Journal

JOHN KEATS.

Journal

Journal

Journal

Journal

John Keats

'Heard melodies are sweet, but
those unheard

Are sweeter...'

– Ode on a Grecian Urn

Journal

Journal

Journal

Journal

Journal

Journal

Journal

Journal

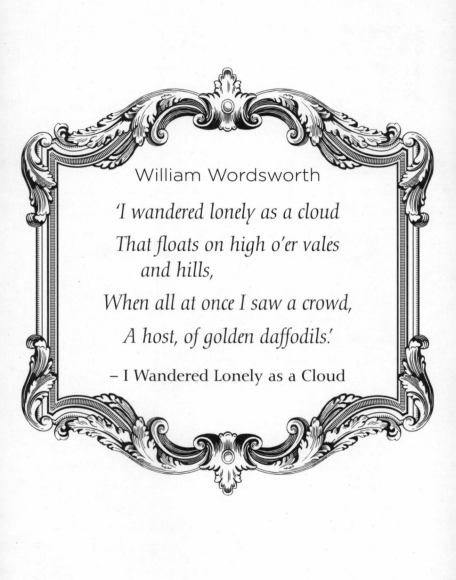

William Wordsworth

'I wandered lonely as a cloud
That floats on high o'er vales
    and hills,
When all at once I saw a crowd,
A host, of golden daffodils.'

– I Wandered Lonely as a Cloud

Journal

Journal

Journal

Journal

Journal

Journal

Journal

Journal

Journal

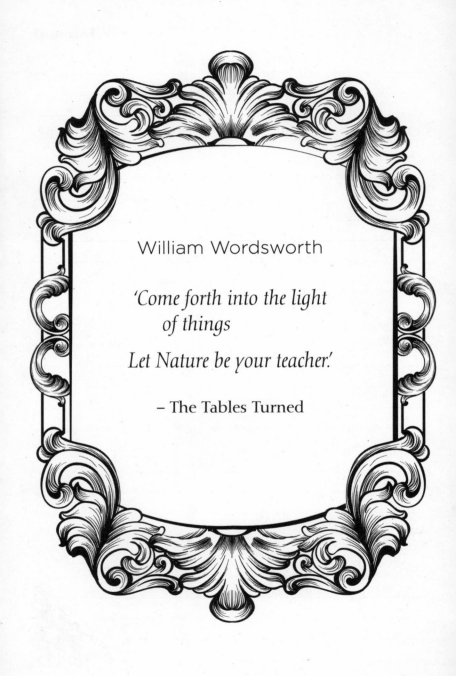

William Wordsworth

'Come forth into the light
of things

Let Nature be your teacher.'

– The Tables Turned

Journal

Journal

Journal

Journal